SUPERIOR MATHEMATICAL PUZZLES

SUPERIOR MATHEMATICAL PUZZLES

WITH DETAILED SOLUTIONS

Howard P. Dinesman

BARNES & NOBLE BOOKS
NEW YORK

2003 Barnes & Noble Books

ISBN 0-7607-3926-9

Printed and bound in the United States of America

03 04 05 06 07 08 MC 9 8 7 6 5 4 3 2 1

BVG

CONTENTS

SUPERIOR MATHEMATICAL PUZZLES

CONTENTS

A BRIEF INTRODUCTION

These puzzles run the gamut from Aristotle's Greece to the missile age. Most are new; some classics are included, too. They are all, I believe, superior in quality to the run-of-the-mill mathematical poser, for they require some sudden insight, some subtle deduction, or some special approach for their solution. There are algebraic puzzles, arithmetical puzzles, geometrical puzzles, and puzzles in logic, in probability, and even three in calculus. They provide an easy and stimulating form of mental exercise. How difficult you will find any particular one cannot be prejudged, for what stumps a sage may be obvious to a student. Your ingenuity, however, *will* be challenged, and the delight of success will be its own reward.

A final note: For those of little self-restraint a tabulation of numerical answers will be found on the very last page. It allows you to peek and "work to an answer" without having the method of solution revealed. The solutions themselves are detailed, clear, and, I trust, correct.

H.P.D.

THE PUZZLES

((1))

COLORFUL COUNTRY

You may have been asked to color in an outline map of the United States. What is the minimum number of colors you will need if no two adjacent states may be the same color?

((2))

MIXED NUTS

Supermarkets and cellophane have supposedly made shopping easy. Just how easy may be judged from your ability to solve this little mix-up.

A package containing 1 pound of walnuts and 2 pounds of Brazils costs $2. One containing 4 pounds of filberts and 1 pound of walnuts costs $3. For only $1.50 you can buy a mixed bag of 3 pounds of almonds, 1 pound of walnuts, and 1 pound of filberts. How much should you pay for a mixture of 1 pound of each of the four kinds?

((3))

TARGET PRACTICE

"Well, Johnny," asked Mrs. Snark, "if a certain missile will hit its target one out of four times, and four such missiles are fired at one target, what is the probability the target will be hit?"

"That's easy," answered Johnny, "it's a certainty one missile will land on target."

Go to the board, young man, and write twenty-five times: *"La théorie de probabilité n'est que le bon sens confirmé par le calcul.* — Marquis de Laplace."

((4))

ON THE LINE

Two subway trains, one twice as fast as the other, set out from opposite ends of the line. They roll nonstop at uniform rates of speed and pass each other at 50th Street. If the faster train is delayed 5 minutes in starting they will meet at a point 2 miles from 50th Street. How fast are the trains moving? How long must the line be?

((5))

MARIENBAD

Several years ago, in a confusing French movie a man wandered the halls of a château beating everyone at an easy-to-play game. Sixteen markers (matchsticks will do) are arrayed in rows of 7, 5, 3, and 1. The two players move in turn, each removing from a single row as many markers as he chooses. (The markers need not be adjacent to be removed; there is no advantage to removing them from the middle of a row.) To win, you must force your opponent to pick up the last remaining marker on the table.

The game was devised by the ancient Chinese and is easy to win at—once you know how. To begin with, do you move first or do you allow your opponent the privilege; or, does it matter? How do you play to win?

((6))

IN THE BALANCE

There are five balls which to the eye and to the touch are identical, although no two of them are the same weight. With only a balance at your disposal can you arrange them in order of weight in a maximum of seven weighings? In other words, determine which is the heaviest, which the second heaviest, and so on.

((7))

GENERATIONS

Fibonacci of Pisa, one of the great mathematicians of the Middle Ages, posed the following question. Its solution has some remarkable ramifications.

"Starting with a single pair of rabbits, which beget a new pair in the first month and each month thereafter, how many pairs will there be at the end of a year if each new pair in each succeeding generation, beginning in their second month, begets another pair each month, and no deaths occur?"

((8))

"DON'T FENCE ME IN"

Three goats graze on a fenced-in meadow containing 120 square yards in the shape of an equal-sided triangle. Each goat is tethered to a stake set in a different corner of the meadow and the tethers are just long enough for a goat to reach the middle of the opposite fence.

If you consider that a goat grazes all the area he alone can reach, half of the area shared by two goats, and one third of the area commonly grazed by all three, how much area in all does one goat graze?

((9))

MULTIPLE DWELLING

Baker, Cooper, Fletcher, Miller, and Smith live on different floors of an apartment house that contains only five floors.

Given the following information can you tell on which floor each one lives?

1. Baker does not live on the top floor.
2. Cooper does not live on the bottom floor.
3. Fletcher does not live on either the top or the bottom floor.
4. Miller lives on a higher floor than does Cooper.
5. Smith does not live on a floor adjacent to Fletcher's.
6. Fletcher does not live on a floor adjacent to Cooper's.

((10))

PIECES OF EIGHT

Captain Kidd decided to reward three officers and seven ordinary pirates for outstanding cutthroatedness. He produced a sack containing 140 gold *reales* and divided them into two unequal piles, giving the larger one to the mates and the smaller to the officers.

The officers counted theirs and found that it contained 2 coins more than could be divided equally among themselves. When the mates tried to divide their pile into seven equal shares they were left with a single coin and soon began to squabble over it. They argued so violently that Kidd himself had to step in and command that the remaining coin be given to the officers.

Now, if each officer received more booty than each mate, how many coins were in each pile?

((11))

A PALINDROME

The honeycomb below conceals one of the most ingenious palindromes ever devised in English. To find it out, start in the center and work your way around from cell to adjacent cell using each of the letters once.

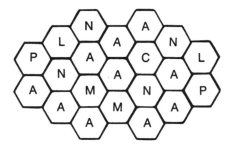

For the uninitiated, a palindrome is a word or phrase which reads the same backward as it does forward. The most famous of all is undoubtedly Napoleon's lament, "Able was I ere I saw Elba."

((12))

TAPER TIMES

One third of an hour after a candle was lighted, the other end was also lighted and it took an additional one third of an hour for the candle to burn out.

If the candle was lighted on both ends at the start, and one end quenched when only the middle one-third of the candle remained, how long in all would it take to burn the candle out?

((13))

THE WATER TOWER PUZZLE

Here is a problem in arithmetical reasoning which will stump not a few readers. If explained patiently it could be understood by a child.

Water is continuously pumped from a reservoir to the town of Mojado, California, at the steady rate of 1,000 gallons per hour. Since the consumption varies throughout the day, the excess, when delivery exceeds demand, is stored in a tower, for use when demand exceeds delivery.

The number of gallons used during eight consecutive three-hour periods is as follows: 2,000, 5,000, 4,500, 2,500, 4,000, 500, 4,000, and 1,500 gallons.

Assuming the water is consumed at a steady rate during each three-hour period, of what capacity must the tower be if the demand is always to be met?

((14))

GRADE CROSSING

Driving from my friend's summer home on Long Island into a nearby village, we were forced to stop at a railroad grade crossing. While waiting for the barriers to be raised after the train had roared by, my host turned to me and said, "That's odd, you know."

"What is?" I asked.

"Well, it seems that on most of the occasions that I've been stopped at this crossing the train has passed by going from west to east, just as it did now."

"There is nothing odd about that, that I can see," I remarked.

"But, look," he said as we drove on, "this is just a branch line and the one train on it shuttles back and forth between the village and the main line terminal. I've checked the schedule, too. The train runs twenty-four hours a day and the ride takes one half hour in either direction."

"What about delays? " I asked, knowing of that line by reputation only.

"None to speak of, and the train waits no longer in one terminal than the other."

"Then, it must be either your imagination or a mere coincidence," I announced smugly. "From what you tell me I calculate that once an hour the train passes the crossing going from west to east, and once an hour it passes it going in the opposite direction. Obviously, you are just as likely to be delayed by a westbound train as by an east-bound one."

"No," he said, "it can't be a coincidence. I have driven up and down this road hundreds of times at all hours of the day and night. There is no pattern to the times I've been stopped at that crossing.

"And it is not my imagination, either," he said sharply as we arrived at our destination. "There must be a rational explanation!"

What is that explanation?

((15))

A MAGIC SQUARE

Below is a seemingly innocent, but highly unusual, magic square. Summed vertically, horizontally, or diagonally the result is 264.

18	99	86	61
66	81	98	19
91	16	69	88
89	68	11	96

In a 4-by-4 magic square such as this one you can also expect the four corner squares, the four interior squares, and each of the four quadrants to reach the same magic total. There are no surprises here.

What, then, is especially magical about this magic square? That is precisely what you are to find out.

((16))

"AMO, AMAS, AMAT . . ."

This question in probability requires greater linguistic skill than mathematical ability:

If the letters of the word *Roma* are arranged randomly in a row, what is the probability they will form a meaningful Latin word?

((17))

THE SHORTEST DISTANCE

After many years of bitter disputes over water rights to the Rio Bravo, the owners of the LBJ and King ranches decided to jointly build a pumping station that would serve both ranches. They agreed amicably on all details except the most important—the location of the station.

King, the less sophisticated mathematician, wanted to keep things simple. "Look here, LBJ," he said, "your ranch is three miles south of the river. Mine is sixteen miles downstream of yours and nine miles south of the river, which runs due east between our spreads. Let's locate the pump at a point on the river shore so that the length of pipeline is the same to either ranch. That shouldn't be hard to figure out and the cost would be the same to both of us."

"There's still a cheaper way," said LBJ. "Somewhere along the shore there is a point where, if we located the pump, the total length of line to both ranches would be less than for any other location. If we shared the cost of both lines equally we'd both save us some money."

"All fine and good," replied King, "but, just where is that point?"

"Give me some time to figure it out," answered LBJ. "I've got to brush up on my calculus."

The next day they met again and LBJ had to confess he hadn't been able to solve the problem. "Let's use your plan," he said, "I can figure that one out."

"Not at all," said King, "your plan is better than mine and I can figure out where to locate the pump without any of that highfalutin calculus of yours!"

How did King solve the problem?

((18))

AN AGE-OLD PROBLEM

Women haven't changed much since ..e first age problem was devised centuries ago; they are still apt to be coy and cryptic in telling their age.

When I asked Sally Slye how old she was she replied: "I am twice as old as my son Si will be when I am seven times as old as Si was when the sum of our ages was twice Si's present age. If you know how old Si is, then you will know how old I am."

When I asked her son his age, he replied: "I, sly Si, Slye scion, am just as old as the sum of the digits in the year in which I was born."

If the year was 1966 when I asked the questions, how old are Sally and Si Slye?

((19))

INTERSECTING LINES

How many triangles are formed when six lines are drawn on a piece of paper so that each line intersects each other line and no three intersect in the same point?

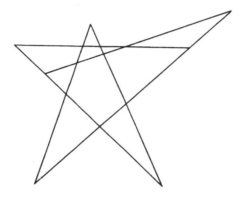

Note: This puzzle will test your ability to count methodically. If you jump headlong into it you may confound yourself.

((20))

A NUMBER OF BOXES

Ernie the shipping clerk was faced with an unusual packing order requiring 100 boxes. Each box was to be in the shape of a cube 1 inch longer on a side than the preceding one, the smallest being 1 inch by 1 inch by 1 inch.

Can you show him an easy way of finding the total area of material required? And while you're at it, the total volume enclosed by the 100 boxes?

((21))

THE SANDS OF TIME

Middle-aged Mary was in a predicament over a pie. The recipe called for baking it exactly nine continuous minutes, but all she had in the way of clocks were two "hour" glasses. The first one measured the lapse of four minutes and the second one seven minutes.

If there are no graduations on the glasses and sand cannot be transferred or removed from them, what is the quickest way Mary can measure nine minutes with the two clocks? (A clock may be stopped by placing it on its side.)

((22))

STARTING PITCHERS

It was the day before the seventh and deciding game of the World Series and the starting pitcher for the Metropolitan nine had not been announced. Though he had already made up his mind, all manager McGrew would say — lest the nominee spend a sleepless night — was that either McGinity, McGivern, or McGillicuddy would be on the mound for the crucial game. McGinity, who knew his way around a craps table, approached the "old man" and said:

"Mr. McGrew, if McGivern's gonna pitch, tell me McGillicuddy ain't gonna. If McGillicuddy's gonna, tell me McGivern ain't. If I'm gonna pitch flip a coin and if it's heads tell me that McGivern ain't gonna, and if it's tails tell me that McGillicuddy ain't gonna. You won't be givin' away any secrets."

"I'll think it over," replied McGrew as he departed into the showers.

Ten minutes later he reappeared, cleared his throat, and announced, "McGillicuddy ain't gonna start."

"I fooled you!" shouted McGinity. "Ten minutes ago I had one chance in three of starting. Now it's between me and McGivern and my chances are up to one in two."

The "old man" smiled, spat, and said, "You're a lousy pitcher McGinity and a lousier mathematician." Then he disappeared into the steam once again.

What are the chances of starting for each pitcher?

((23))

A NUMBER SEQUENCE

New Yorkers will have little trouble with this puzzle. Simply supply the next term in the sequence: 14, 34, 42, 72, ____.

If your train of thought puts you on the wrong track you must pay the consequences.

((24))

ZAMBEZI FALLS

At Zambezi Falls the upper Zambezi River becomes the lower Zambezi River. The falls are really a series of cataracts, each one dropping $\frac{1}{7}$ the distance of the preceding one, *ad infinitum*. If the first cataract drops a distance of $66\frac{2}{3}$ feet, what is the difference in elevation between the upper and lower Zambezi Rivers?

((25))

THE GALLOWS

When Sancho Panza was governor of the island of Barataria a man was brought before him, his fate to be decided. It seems there was a bridge across a river in Sancho's domain, with a gallows and a court of justice of sorts at one end. Anyone wishing to cross had to swear to the truth of his destination. The gallows awaited anyone who swore falsely. The man in question had declared, "I am destined to die on the gallows erected upon this bridge."

Clearly, if he was telling the truth he must be allowed to pass, turning the truth into a lie; and if he was lying he must be hanged, turning his lie into the truth; and this is why the perplexed justices brought him before the Honorable Sancho Panza.

How was his fate decided?

((26))

MEXICAN JUMPING BEANS

Humberto Rojo y Negro, the notorious Mexican bandit, once confronted me armed with nothing more than three identical boxes and six jumping beans—three red and three black, of course. With these simple articles he posed two very stimulating brainteasers. Fortunately, my life was not staked on the outcome of that mathematical challenge.

While my back was turned he placed two beans in each of the boxes and labeled one box "RB" (for Red-Black), the second "RR," and the last one "BB."

"Now, my friend," he said, setting the closed boxes before me, "not one of these little boxes has a truthful sign on it. I will allow you to pick one bean at a time from any box you choose—without looking into the box, of course. The problem for you is to find out which beans are in each box. But, I warn you, I will not let you make more picks than is really necessary!"

After a few minutes thought I was able to solve the puzzle. "Too easy!" I exclaimed.

Señor Rojo was undismayed. "Now, let us, as they say in your country, separate the men from the boys."

He then removed the labels from the boxes and placed two red beans in one box, two black beans in a second, and a red and a black bean in the third. After closing the lids he shuffled the boxes before me.

"Pick any box you wish and take one bean from it," he instructed me.

I drew a red bean.

"What," he asked, "are the chances that the second bean in the box you have chosen is also red?"

"The red bean I have drawn must come from either the 'Red-Red' box or the 'Red-Black' box," I reasoned aloud, "and since it is just as likely that I have selected one box as the other, the chances are even — fifty-fifty — that the second bean is also red.

"That one is too easy also," I added.

The bandit smiled. "No, my friend, not easy; difficult."

((27))

A LOGICAL DEDUCTION

A. There are five lettered statements in this puzzle.

B. This is not a statement.

C. Only two of the statements are false.

D. Only one of them is true.

E. If you can solve this puzzle you are a very logical person.

Is statement E true?

((28))

TOUR DU MONDE

The equator and two circles of longitude ninety degrees apart will divide the globe into eight identical zones. Starting in a given zone, in how many different ways is it possible to take a trip around the world passing through each of the eight zones once, and only once, ending up where you started? You are not permitted to enter a zone by crossing the equator diagonally or by going over the poles.

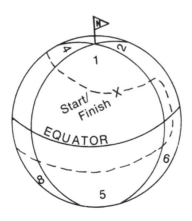

((29))

THE COURIER

This is a classic puzzle in algebra which has appeared in many collections and goes back to antiquity. If you have never seen it before, it deserves your attention now.

A courier starting at the rear of a moving army 100 miles long rides to the front, delivers a message, and rides immediately to the rear, where he finds he is 100 miles ahead of his starting point.

In all, how far did he ride? Of course, the army was moving at a steady pace all the time and the courier's speed was constant.

((30))

SEMAPHORE SIGNALS

When Connie Mack was managing the Philadelphia Athletics at Shibe Park he shunned the use of the bullpen telephone. If he wanted Bobby Schantz he would signal by ruffling his pants. For Carl Shibe to warm up he'd point to the ballpark stands.

He was lucky he had such "poetic" pitchers. I knew of a team deep in the bush leagues that had no bullpen phone and was not so fortunate in the names (or the abilities) of its pitchers. The manager, an old Signal Corpsman, had to rig up a semaphore system. I remember that he had two identical red flags, two identical blue flags, and two identical white flags, and he would hoist from one to six of them up a pole, one beneath the other with no spacing. For the sake of clarity he never hoisted two flags of the same color adjacent to one another.

Can you tell how many distinct signals were possible with that system?

((31))

THE TWELVE-FINGER TRIBE

In the remotest area of the Pyrenees lives a tribe of people rarely seen by idle tourists. Strangely enough, these descendants of the original Iberians have six fingers on each hand. And not so strangely, their number system contains twelve digits (including zero) compared with our own ten-digit, or *decimal,* system. The digits from 0 thru 9 are written the same way in both systems. The figures T and L are used by the Iberians to represent ten and eleven, respectively, the two extra digits in their system.

In our number system we count by groups of ten, in theirs—called the *duodecimal*—by groups of twelve. For example:

our	12	is duodecimal	10	(one group of twelve plus zero units)
"	30	"	26	
"	136	"	L4	(eleven groups of twelve, plus four)
"	144	"	100	
the sum	322	"	22T	and so on.

The puzzles for your consideration number three. The first two demonstrate the compatibility of the duodecimal system with the English system of measure (and conversely, the reason why scientists prefer to use metric measure with our decimal system). The third one should prove how difficult it is to use an unfamiliar system.

A) The twelve-finger tribe's baker received orders for 49, 68, T2, LL, and 100 loaves of bread. How does he easily know how many loaves to bake?

B) Can you show how readily the area in square feet of a table 2 ft. 5¼ in. by 3 ft. 1⅓ in. may be calculated using duodecimal notation?

C)

```
            7   L
   (×)      _   _
            _   _   _
        _   _   _
      _____
        _   2   _   _
(−)         _   _   2
        1   9   6   6
```

Complete this combination duodecimal multiplication and subtraction by filling in the blanks with any of the digits 0 thru L.

((32))

A VISIT TO ANOTHER PLANET

The planet Topsis is unusual in that each "hemisphere" is a right-circular cone of height 3,000 miles and base radius 4,000 miles. The two cones are joined base to base so that the equator is the base circle and the vertical distance between the poles is 6,000 miles.

Since the days of interplanetary travel are not too far off, and as an Earthman you might at first have a little difficulty getting around on Topsis, here is a problem to help you develop their system of navigation:

Topsy and Turvy are two cities located on the equator 180 degrees apart. What is the shortest distance between them?

((33))

SPINNING REELS

Aunt Matilda thought it would be fun to show the movies she took last summer in Hawaii. Exactly 5 minutes and 20 seconds after starting, when the take-up reel was rotating 1½ times as fast as the projecting reel, the film broke. How many thrilling minutes of travelogue did we miss?

((34))

ODDBALL OUT

This old chestnut concerns twelve balls. Eleven of them are identical in every way, while the twelfth can be distinguished only by its weight.

Using only a balance, can you determine which of the twelve is the oddball and whether it is heavier or lighter than the others? You are allowed no more than three weighings!

((35))

THE DEADWOOD STAGE

The stagecoach from Tucson to Deadwood is direct, but there is one 30-minute stopover at a way station. If you set out on foot from Tucson at the same time the stage did, you would be 4 miles from Tucson when the stage reached the station, and you would arrive at the station just when the coach pulled out; if you continued walking, you would be 1 mile from Deadwood when the coach arrived there. If, however, you boarded the stage when you got to the way station, it would take you 15 minutes longer to get from Tucson to Deadwood than if you rode the stage to the station and immediately set out on foot for Deadwood.

How far is it from Tucson to Deadwood?

((36))

MIDWAY MAGIC

Charley Barker, the midway man, was good at guessing figures. He could guess your weight within 5 pounds or your age within 2 years. When business was slow he would pull out his slate and do a little number guessing. He would ask you to write down the year of your birth; to form any new number by rearranging the digits; then to find the difference between the two numbers and multiply it by your age in years. This done, you were to erase all your calculations and one digit from your answer. With a flourish (and for a fee) Charley would conjure up the missing digit nine times out of ten.

If you were still game, he would ask you to make up as many numbers as you pleased from the nine digits and zero, provided that each digit was used once, and only once. (E.g., 9, 321, 45, 60.7, and 8.) He then instructed you to add up all the numbers and multiply the sum by your weight to the nearest pound. Then again, you were to erase all your work and one digit from your answer. Nine out of ten times he had you here too.

I have followed Charley Barker's instructions and my results are 55__7.43 for the first trick and 171,__17 for the second. Can you figure out the midway man's method and "guess" the missing numbers?

((37))

THE AMOROUS OCTOPI

All right, in just how many different ways can two eight-tentacled octopi kiss?

((38))

MATCHSTICKS

Using 12 matchsticks, can you construct a plane figure containing an area of exactly 3 square matchstick lengths?

((39))

HUNGARIAN ROULETTE

A scurrilous saying has it that if you have a Hungarian for a friend you will not want for enemies. Here is a game allegedly played among friends in old Budapest.

Two chambers of a six-shot revolver are selected at random and loaded. The cylinder is spun once and two adjacent chambers are fired, one for each player. Needless to say, if the first shot is fatal, the second player does not try his luck.

If you are sensible enough to figure out your chances but mad enough to play, would you go first or second? What are the chances that both players survive?

((40))

NEWTON'S *PROBLEMA BOVINUM*

A farmer was puzzled by the fact that 24 of his cows would graze 10 acres bare in 2 weeks, but 12 cows would take not 4 but 6 weeks to graze the same pasture bare. "I wonder," he mused, "how long it would take 12 cows to graze 20 acres bare?"

Can you solve the farmer's puzzle?

The "farmer" was Sir Isaac Newton, and he posed it in his *Arithmetica Universalis* (1707).

The grass at the start in each case is, of course, at the same height, and each cow eats the same amount every day. You have probably already surmised that the steady growth of the grass must be considered!

((41))

FLIGHT CREW

Scott, Carpenter, Gordon, and Cooper make up a flight crew—pilot, copilot, navigator, and engineer—but not necessarily in that order. Assign the right man to the right job on the basis of the following information, some of which may be of no help to you.

1. The pilot and copilot are good friends.
2. Scott and Cooper are not good friends.
3. The engineer's wife is a passenger.
4. Scott and Cooper do not wear glasses.
5. But I'm not sure about Carpenter or Gordon.
6. Only Gordon and Cooper are married.
7. Gordon had lunch with the copilot.
8. The pilot doesn't wear glasses.
9. But the navigator does.
10. The navigator is engaged to the stewardess.
11. The stewardess is good-looking.

((42))

JOINT VENTURE

Three boys formed a partnership to sell newspapers. They agreed that each boy would keep one half the profits on the papers he sold, with the other half going into a pool to be shared equally by all three.

On Monday Johnny sold twice as many papers as Willy did and found that his total earnings after the pool was split were a dollar less than Willy's and Sammy's combined. On Tuesday if Willy and Sammy were to sell the same number of papers as they did on the previous day, and if Johnny were to sell 25 more than all three did on Monday, his total earnings on Tuesday would then equal Willy's and Sammy's combined for Tuesday.

If each boy buys his papers 5 for 4 cents and sells them for 2 cents apiece, how many papers did each boy sell on Monday?

((43))

THE MEDLEY RACE

Dolph and Flip swam a 100-yard medley race: the first lap (50 yards) backstroke and the return lap free style. Dolph gave Flip an 8-second head start and beat him by 14 yards. When Flip was 2 yards short of completing his first lap he met Dolph swimming the other way. Both swimmers can free-style 1½ times as fast as they can backstroke.

The question to be answered — and it is a tricky one — is this: How many yards head start can Dolph afford to give Flip and still not lose?

((44))

UPS AND DOWNS

A man can walk up a moving "up" escalator in ½ minute. He can walk down this moving "up" escalator in 1½ minutes. If his walking pace is the same up stairs as it is down stairs, how long would it take him to climb the escalator stairs if it was not moving? How long would it take him to go up the moving escalator if he stood still?

((45))

BATTING AVERAGES

There's no way in which a bad ballplayer can hide his ineptitude. Every day, for all to see, his accomplishments are reported in the newspaper sports pages.

Suppose we were all subject to such publicity! There in bold print we might read, "Willy Lomans, salesman, saw 8 customers yesterday and made only 1 sale to reduce his season's average to .163" or, "Tom Jones dated Lorna Doom last night and struck out, making the twelfth consecutive time he has failed to get to first base."

Oh well, I looked up the batting statistics of a certain Metropolitan shortstop and noticed that if he had as many hits as he has at-bats, and as many at-bats as the sum of his hits and his at-bats, his average would be 1½ times as great as it would be if his at-bats were reduced by the number of hits he has.

If a ballplayer's batting average is determined by dividing his hits by his at-bats, what is the shortstop's average?

((46))

BUYER BEWARE

Buck Fuller, the well-known speculator, was down on his luck. "Quick Buck," as he was known along "The Street," was down to his last thousand as well.

"I might as well," he thought, "have a little extra fun for my money." And he called at his broker's to place an order.

"I want Zoom Missiles at thirty, Blackout Power at twenty, and Bonanza Uranium at fifty cents."

"How many of each?" the broker asked.

"I want a total of a hundred shares and I don't care how you split them up. And, oh yes, the total value is to be exactly one thousand dollars."

The broker took the order with a weary smile. "Another of your puzzles, right, Buck? Well, you haven't stumped me yet, and I'll figure this one out, too."

The next week's papers were full of stories about missile "gaps," power failures, and uranium strikes. Buck's missiles zoomed, his utilities hummed, and his uraniums fairly fissioned. They doubled and redoubled in value. Satisfied at last, he called again at his broker's.

"Sell!" cried Buck.

"Sell what?" replied the broker.

"My stocks. The ones I ordered. The ones you bought for me."

"But Buck," replied the broker, smiling all the while, "I never bought them. You stumped me at last."

How many stocks of each kind should the broker have purchased?

((47))

A FISHY STORY

Back from Baja California, my fishing friend Oscar Gadabout regaled me with the story of his catch of a 125-pound marlin. When I doubted his tale he became angry, said he had proof, and showed me a photograph taken at the weighing.

The photo showed the fish tied by the tail to one end of a rope which passed over a pulley. Oscar had hoisted the marlin and then tied the other end of the rope to the dock beneath the pulley. There was a big smile on his face and sure enough the scale from which the pulley was suspended read 125 pounds. When I told him how much his catch really weighed, he really became angry. What was Oscar's mistake?

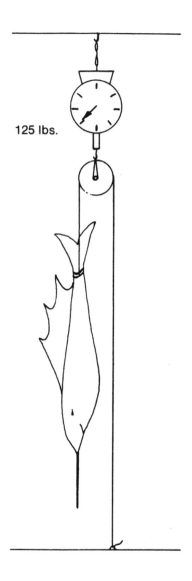

125 lbs.

((48))

PETER PIPER'S PUZZLE

Everyone knows that Peter Piper picked a peck of pickled peppers. But, just how long did it take him?

We know that Peter and his friend Paul, working together, could pick a peck in 20 minutes; Paul and his friend Priam, working together, could do the job in 30 minutes; while it would take 40 minutes for Peter and Priam to pick a peck together.

((49))

"UNION FOREVER . . ."

Down on the village green, opposite the Civil War monument, thirty cannonballs, each 1 foot in diameter, are stacked into a square-based pyramid. It is a neat puzzle to try and determine the vertical height of the pyramid, measured from the ground to the top of the topmost cannonball.

((50))

". . . AND EVER"

If all thirty cannonballs of the previous puzzle were rearranged to form two regular tetrahedrons (triangular pyramids, the bases and all sides of which are equal-angled triangles) what would be the height of the taller one, measured as before?

((51))

THE DUEL

Because of a now forgotten slander, Mr. J. challenged Mr. K. to a duel. Peeved at not being consulted in the matter, M. de G. challenged both the aforementioned gentlemen. Pistols were selected and a three-way duel was agreed upon, arranged as follows:

1. Each gentleman stands at one corner of an equal-sided triangle, 100 paces from either opponent.
2. Each gentleman shoots in turn — a single shot — at anyone he chooses.
3. The order of shooting is chosen by lot.
4. The duel continues in this order until there remains but one survivor.

Mr. J. and Mr. K. were both crack shots and never missed at that distance. M. de G., a neophyte at weaponry, could hit his mark only 60 per cent of the time. If all three dueled wisely and well, who probably survived?

((52))

HUXLEY'S MONKEYS

The biologist Thomas Huxley (1825-1895) is generally credited with having first made the oft-repeated statement that if you set six monkeys at six typewriters they would *eventually* write the works of Shakespeare. Huxley was illustrating the role of chance in the evolutionary process.

Well, then, if a monkey set at a typewriter strikes each of the 26 upper-case letters once, and only once, what is the probability that somewhere in the random array 4 successive letters will spell left to right the names "IAGO" or "LEAR"?

((53))

AROUND THE SILO

If you butted your head on Puzzle Number 8, here is a difficult opportunity to make amends.

A goat is tethered to the outside wall of a circular silo 20 feet in diameter. If the length of the tether is such that it will just wind halfway around the silo, how large an area around the silo is the goat able to graze on?

((54))

THE MOONSHINE CAPER

Ol' Rufus snuck down to the still one dark night to tap a 100-gallon cask of 100 per cent pure moonshine. Cagey as he was, he replaced what he stole with creek water. As he tapped the cask, he poured the water in through the top at the same rate at which he was filling his 10-gallon can, keeping the contents of the cask constantly stirred.

If the whole caper took 10 minutes, precisely how many gallons of moonshine and how many of water did Rufus run off with in his 10-gallon can?

((55))

PURSUIT — A Puzzle for Cold Warriors

An enemy ship is 3 miles due east of the nuclear sub *Piranha* and proceeding due north at a uniform rate of speed. At this instant a sonar-homing torpedo is fired directly at the foe. The guidance system controls the torpedo so that at every instant it is aimed directly at the target.

If the speed of the torpedo is twice that of the target vessel — which tries no evasive tactics — how far will it travel in pursuit before hitting it?

((56))

THE SPIDER AND THE FLY

This is probably the best-known puzzle created by the prolific Britisher Henry Dudeney (1847-1930). Try it and see why.

Inside a rectangular room 30 feet long, 12 feet wide, and 12 feet high, a spider eyes his supper.

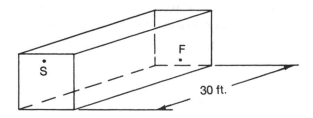

The spider is located on one end wall, halfway between the side walls, 1 foot from the ceiling. The unsuspecting fly rests directly opposite on the other end wall, 1 foot from the floor.

What is the shortest distance the spider must crawl to get his supper? (He must crawl the entire way—no webs, please!)

((57))

SAM LOYD'S FERRYBOAT PUZZLE

Two ferryboats, one faster than the other, set out at the same time from opposite shores of a river. They meet at a point 720 yards from the near shore and continue on to the terminals. There they spend 10 minutes discharging and picking up passengers before setting out again.

If the boats meet the second time at a point 400 yards from the far shore, how wide is the river?

The nicety of this puzzle is the simplicity of the solution. Yet, Loyd* would "hazard the opinion that ninety-nine out of every hundred of our shrewdest businessmen would fail to solve it in a week. So much for learning mathematics by rule instead of common sense, which teaches the reason why!"

*See the solution to Puzzle Number 35

((58))

THE BIRTHDAY PUZZLE

Many people who know little of mathematics are familiar with the surprising answer to this puzzle. It is probably fair to say that few of them know that it was introduced by George Gamow (1904-) distinguished astronomer, author of *One, Two, Three . . . Infinity,* and, not insignificantly, puzzle enthusiast.

The puzzle is simple to state, but not so simply solved:

Thirty people gather at random in a room. How likely is it that among them two people will share the same birthday (month and day)?

((59))

THE MONKEY PUZZLE

Lewis Carroll, Oxford mathematician, created, as is well known, the adventures of *Alice in Wonderland.* He also created quite a stir with this seemingly simple question:

If a weight suspended from a rope which passes over a pulley is exactly balanced by a monkey hanging on the other end of the rope, what happens to the weight if the monkey tries to climb the rope? (Assume the rope and pulley are weightless and frictionless; also, that the rope is perfectly flexible and inextensible.)

This was reputedly one of Carroll's two favorite puzzles. Down to the present day it has perplexed and chagrined many a learned man. It is your turn now.

((60))

THE TOWER ESCAPE

A queen, her son, and her daughter were held cap-
tive in the top room of a tall tower. Outside their window
was a pulley with a rope around it and two baskets of equal
weight, one at each end of the rope. The length of the rope
was such that the one basket coming down would raise the
other basket just to the height of the window. They man-
aged to make their escape by means of this system and a
weight they found in their room. It was quite safe to lower
themselves in the basket if they weighed no more than 15
pounds more than the contents of the lower basket.

How did they manage to do it if the queen weighed
195 pounds, the daughter 165 pounds, the son 90 pounds,
and the weight 75 pounds?

The problem is complicated by the fact that the
queen had with her in the room, besides her two children
and the weight, a pig weighing 60 pounds, a dog 45
pounds, and a cat 30 pounds. These had to be lowered
safely, too, with the same restrictions. The weight can be
brought down any way of course, but there must be someone at each end to put the animals into and out of the baskets, though they need not be tended to otherwise.

((61))

"IT CAN'T BE DONE!"

Using only a straight edge and a compass and with all the time in the world, how can you trisect any angle?

THE SOLUTIONS

((1))

The schematic diagram of the seven most westerly adjacent states (below) requires a minimum of four colors for segregation.

Since no one has ever been able to draw a map that needed more than four colors, we can assume without further trial that the entire map of the states can be completed with those four colors. Nevertheless, a satisfactory proof of this "four-color theorem" still evades those who toil in the branch of mathematics called *topology*.

((2))

It is impossible to determine the cost per pound of each of the four commodities. You can, however, determine the cost of various combinations of them.

If you combine 1½ packages of the first kind ($3) with ½ package of the second ($1.50) and all of the third package ($1.50), you get 3 pounds of each for $6. A mixture of 1 pound of each should cost you $2.

((3))

Common sense tells you that if each missile has a chance to miss, there is a chance all four will miss. Also, that the target may be hit by either one, two, three, or all four missiles.

Laplace now reminds us to "confirm by calculation," for sometimes common sense deceives us, genius as well as Johnny. (It was no less a mathematician than Leibniz, codeveloper of the calculus, who asserted that a *twelve* was just as likely as an *eleven* on the roll of two dice!)

Since each missile has 3 chances in 4 of missing, the probability all four will miss is:

$$\tfrac{3}{4} \times \tfrac{3}{4} \times \tfrac{3}{4} \times \tfrac{3}{4} = \tfrac{81}{256}$$

The probability the target will *not* be missed is:

$$1 - \tfrac{81}{256} = \tfrac{175}{256}$$

(The 175 chances include hits by one, two, three, and all four missiles.)

((4))

The common assumption that one train goes 2 miles in 5 minutes, or 24 mph, is incorrect.

A better assumption (for the purpose of finding the speed of the trains) is that when the slower train reaches 50th Street the faster train is X miles away, and that if the slower train waited at 50th Street the faster train would travel the X miles in 5 minutes. But the slower train goes 2 miles farther before they meet, and in that time the faster train travels twice as far, or 4 miles. Therefore, X = 6 miles; the faster train's speed is 6 miles in 5 minutes, or 72 mph, and the slower train's speed is 3 miles in 5 minutes, or 36 mph.

The length of the line could be any distance greater than 3 miles. At that length the slower train would arrive at the terminal just when the faster train begins to pull out, 5 minutes late.

Now puzzle this: If, instead, the *slower* train is delayed 5 minutes in starting, they still will meet at a point 2 miles from 50th Street.

84

((5))

Allow your opponent the first play. If he removes 2 or more markers you can always counter with a move that leaves a winning combination of rows. Simple winning combinations are 5-4-1, 3-2-1, and 1-1-1. Any combination of pairs (5-5, 4-4-1-1, and so on), with the obvious exceptions of 1-1 and 1-1-1-1, are also winners.

When leaving paired rows you simply match your opponent's moves until you have the opportunity to leave him the last marker. For example, if you leave 5-5-1-1, and he removes 3 from one row, you remove 3 from the paired row, leaving 2-2-1-1. Regardless of his next move you can win.

Any move your opponent makes on a 5-4-1 combination can be converted by you to a 3-2-1 or a 1-1-1, or a paired-row combination. The value of 3-2-1 or 1-1-1 combinations should be apparent.

If your opponent removes only 1 marker at a time, you match his moves by removing 1 marker at a time from an *untouched* row, until 2 or more markers have been removed from any single row. He will always make the fatal move, on either his second or his third play. Then again, with a little thought you can find a winning combination and play to a successful conclusion. *Note:* The starting array—7, 5, 3, 1—is itself a winning combination; that is why the strategy for winning at this little *divertissement* requires you to play second.

((6))

If you place the five balls in order, one ball at a time, it will take you a maximum of eight weighings. Here is how to do it in seven:

1. Weigh any two balls against each other. Label them *H* (heavier) and *L* (lighter).
2. Weigh any two of the remaining three balls against each other. Label them *h* and *l*.

3. Weigh *H* against *h*. (Assume for this explanation that *H* is heavier.) You now have three balls in order: *H, h, l*. Put *L* aside.

4&5. In a maximum of two weighings you can place the fifth ball in order among *H, h, l*.

6&7. Regardless of the placement of the fifth ball you can position *L* in a maximum of two weighings, making judicious use of the knowledge that *L* is lighter than *H*.

((7))

One pair is born in each of the first two months. During the third month 2 pairs are born. Then 3 pairs are born in the fourth month, 5 in the fifth, and 8 in the sixth.

By writing in order the number of pairs born each month, we obtain the famous sequence

$$1, 1, 2, 3, 5, 8, 13, \ldots$$

known as "Fibonacci's Progression."

Notice that each term in the progression after the first two equals the sum of the two preceding terms. Thus, the twelfth term is 144; and the number of pairs living at the end of the year is twice 144, plus the number of immature pairs (89) born in the eleventh month, or 377 in all.

In fact, 377 is the fourteenth term of the Fibonacci Progression, and the number of pairs living in any month, starting with the first, form the progression

$$2, 3, 5, 8, 13, 21, \ldots$$

One of the remarkable characteristics of the Fibonacci Progression is its relationship to the "Golden Ratio" of art history.

Briefly, the dimensions of a rectangle (or painting) are thought to be the most aesthetically satisfying if the ratio of the width (W) to the depth (D) is such that $\frac{W}{D} = \frac{D}{W + D}$. The ratio $\frac{W}{D}$ is then called "golden"; its numerical value is $\frac{\sqrt{5} - 1}{2} = .61803 \ldots$

Now, it happens that the ratio of any two consecutive terms in the Fibonacci Progression approaches the Golden Ratio. The

86

convergence is quite rapid, too: using the sixth and seventh terms, the ratio $^8/_{13} = .61538$ . . . The Fibonacci Progression and its multiples thereby allow the artist to readily select the dimensions of his canvas as close to the Golden Ratio as he pleases.

((8))

As any farmer can tell you, since the entire meadow is grazed and each goat can reach the same amount of area as the next one can, one goat grazes $^1/_3$ of 120 square yards, or 40 square yards.

((9))

From top to bottom live Miller, Fletcher, Baker, Cooper, and Smith.

A sensible method of solving puzzles of this type is to use a simple table called a *matrix*.

		FLOOR				
		1	2	3	4	5
BAKER	A					X
COOPER	B	X	X	X		
FLETCHER	C	X	X	X		
MILLER	D	X	X			
SMITH	E			X		

Each box in the matrix represents a possible occupancy for one of the men. When all but one box in a row or column are eliminated, the remaining box is a definite occupancy.

Condition 1 eliminates A5. The second condition eliminates B1. C1 and C5 are eliminated by the third; D1, D2, and B5 by the fourth; and E3 by the fifth. Boxes B3 and C3 are eliminated by condition 6.

At this point it is necessary to proceed by trial. Assume, for example, that Baker lives on the 1st floor. This eliminates A2, A3, A4, and E1, leaving only Miller for the 3rd floor and then only Smith for the 5th. Cooper and Fletcher cannot now be placed in the remaining boxes without violating condition 4 or 5. Place an X in box A1 and you are on your way.

SUPERIOR MATHEMATICAL PUZZLES

((10))

Let X be the equal share from the smaller pile and Y be the equal share from the larger one. Then $3X + 2$ is the number of coins in the smaller pile, and $7Y + 1$ is the number in the larger one. Thus,

$$(3X + 2) + (7Y + 1) = 140$$
$$3X + 7Y = 137 \qquad \text{(I)}$$

What we are looking for is an integer solution in X and Y of equation I. Moreover, $7Y + 1$ must be greater than $3X + 2$; and since each officer received more than each mate did, $X + 1$ must be greater than Y.

Equations of this type requiring integer solutions are called *Diophantine* equations, after the Greek algebraist Diophantus (3rd century A.D.). The analysis which follows is also called *Diophantine.*

Divide both sides of the equation by the coefficient 3, and let Q denote an integer:

$$X + 2Y + \tfrac{Y}{3} = 45 + \tfrac{2}{3}$$

Since X, 2Y, and 45 are integers

$$\tfrac{Y}{3} - \tfrac{2}{3} = Q$$
$$Y - 2 = 3Q$$
$$Y = 3Q + 2 \qquad \text{(II)}$$

Substitute equation II into equation I to get

$$3X = 137 - 21Q - 14$$
$$X = 41 - 7Q \qquad \text{(III)}$$

The equation is now solved. By selecting values of the integer Q, equations II and III will yield integer values of X and Y which satisfy equation I.

The six positive integer solutions (obtained by letting $Q = 0$, 1, 2, 3, 4, and 5) are

X	41	34	27	20	13	6
Y	2	5	8	11	14	17

Of these only the solution $X = 20$, $Y = 11$ meets the two conditions mentioned above. The officers' pile therefore contained 62 coins, and the mates' pile contained 78. Each officer received 21 coins; each mate 11.

Incidentally, the most famous Diophantine equation of all is
$$X^n + Y^n = Z^n$$
(Where $n = 2$ we have the Pythagorean relationship for right triangles. One particular Diophantine solution would be $X = 3$, $Y = 4$, $Z = 5$.)

Fermat, the great seventeenth-century French mathematician, in a note in the margin of a book discovered after his death, asserted that the equation had no integer solutions where n is greater than 2. His proof, he wrote, was too long to fit into the margin, and to this day no one has ever been able to prove or disprove "Fermat's Last Theorem."

((11))

The hidden palindrome is
A MAN, A PLAN, A CANAL: PANAMA.
It was devised by James Thurber.

((12))

The second way is really the first way backwards. It, too, would take $2/3$ of an hour to burn the candle out.

((13))

The deficit incurred (−) or surplus gained (+) during each 3-hour period is the 3,000-gallon input minus the use during the period. In consecutive order these net flows are + 1,000, − 2,000, − 1,500, + 500, − 1,000, + 2,500, − 1,000, and + 1,500 gallons.

Since the flow is continuous, day in and day out, it does not matter where you start, only that you stay in order.

Let Q be the amount in the tower at the start of the 1st period. At the end of the 1st period there will be Q + 1,000; at the end of the 2nd there will be (Q + 1,000) − 2,000 = Q − 1,000; at the end of the 3rd through 8th periods, respectively, there will be Q − 2,500, Q − 2,000, Q − 3,000, Q − 500, Q − 1,500, and Q gallons.

89

Q must be at least 3,000 gallons, or the town will run dry during the 5th period. The maximum in the tower at any time is Q + 1,000 gallons at the end of the 1st period. The minimum capacity of the tower must therefore be 3,000 + 1,000 = 4,000 gallons.

((14))

There is indeed a rational explanation to this puzzle: The grade crossing must be located closer to the eastern terminal than to the western terminal. Then, at any given time the train is more likely to be west of the crossing than east of it since a greater portion of the line lies in that direction and the train spends a greater portion of the one-hour round trip on it. When west of the crossing, whether heading east or west, the train will next pass the grade crossing going from west to east.

What is confusing, of course, is that the train will regularly make the same number of westbound passes of the crossing as it will eastbound passes. Electrical engineers will no doubt recognize this as a confusion of *frequency* and *phase*, but lack of special training (pun intended) is no excuse for having missed this one.

((15))

This magic square can be read as a magic square even when turned upside down!

((16))

There are $4 \times 3 \times 2 \times 1 = 24$ possible arrangements of the letters R, O, M, and A. According to W. S. Jevons (1835-1882), the logician who first posed this curiosity, 7 of the 24 are significant: *ramo, mora, armo,* and the palindromic pairs *Roma* and *amor,* and *oram* and *maro.*

90

((17))

Place an imaginary King ranch 18 miles due north of the real one, so that the south shore of the river runs halfway between them. Observe that no matter where along the south shore you locate the station, it will be exactly as far from the real King ranch as from the imaginary one. Thus, the total distance from the LBJ ranch to the station to *either* the real or imaginary King ranch will be the same. Since the shortest distance from the LBJ to the imaginary King ranch is a straight line drawn between them, locate the station where this line intersects the south shore!

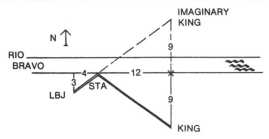

It will be seen from similar triangles that the two pipelines make the same angle with the river, so that the station is 4 miles downstream of the LBJ ranch and the total length of line is 20 miles.

((18))

Si was born in 1946 and is 20 years old. Sally's age is unknown and cannot, like Si's, be readily determined by trial. Call it X.

Now we are dealing with three different times — the present, a time in the future Y years from now, and a time in the past Z years ago. It remains to translate the verbiage into algebraic equalities:

"I am twice as old as my son will be . . ." becomes
$X = 2 (20 + Y)$;
". . . when I am seven times as old as Si was . . ."
becomes $X + Y = 7 (20 - Z)$; and
". . . when the sum of our ages was twice Si's pres-

ent age" becomes $(X - Z) + (20 - Z) = 2(20)$.

Simultaneous solution of these three equations reveals Sally Slye to be a spry 46. The times referred to are 13 years ago and 3 years from now.

((19))

No matter how you draw the lines, if they meet the conditions of the problem, 20 triangles are formed.

Each group of 3 lines forms a triangle. The number of groups of 6 lines taken 3 at a time is $\frac{6 \times 5 \times 4}{3 \times 2 \times 1} = 20$ groups. If you tried to count them without method you probably missed a few.

((20))

The total area can be calculated quickly if you remember that the sum of the squares of the first n numbers is $S = \frac{n + 3n^2 + 2n^3}{6}$. In this case the total area is $6S$ — there being six sides to each box — where n is 100.

Area $= 100 + 3(100)^2 + 2(100)^3 = 2{,}030{,}100$ square inches.

The total volume of the boxes is the sum of the cubes of the numbers 1 through 100. In the identity $1^3 + 2^3 + 3^3 + \ldots + n^3 = (1 + 2 + 3 \ldots + n)^2$ it is a simple matter to evaluate the right-hand side, an arithmetic progression, for $n = 100$.

Volume $= (\frac{1 + 100}{2} \times 100)^2 = 25{,}502{,}500$ cubic inches.

				Row No.	
			1	1	
		3	5	2	
	7	9	11	3	
13	15	17	19	4	
	.		.	.	
	.		.	.	
M	....		L	$\frac{n}{S}$	

Here is an artful proof of that identity attributed to Fibonacci. (See Puzzle Number 7.) It uses the odd-number triangle shown at the left.

Note that the number of terms in each row equals the row number. The total number of terms in the triangle through any row, n, is the sum $S = 1 + 2 + 3 \ldots + n$ which is $\dfrac{(1 + n)n}{2}$. The last term in the nth row, L, is $2S - 1$; the first term, M, is $L - 2(n - 1)$. The sum of the numbers in any row, n, is

$$\frac{(M + L)\, n}{2} = \frac{(2L - 2n + 2)\, n}{2} = (2S - n)\, n = n^3$$

Therefore, the sum $1^3 + 2^3 + 3^3 \ldots + n^3$ is the sum of the numbers in all of the rows 1 through n—it is the sum of all the numbers in the triangle. The numbers are in arithmetic progression and their sum is

$$\frac{(1 + L)\, S}{2} = S^2 = (1 + 2 + 3 \ldots + n)^2 \qquad Q.E.D.$$

The identity used to calculate the total area of the boxes, namely $1^2 + 2^2 + 3^2 \ldots + n^2 = \dfrac{n + 3n^2 + 2n^3}{6}$, can be proved using the number triangle shown below. It was known in ancient India. Go to it, if it be your puzzle pleasure.

1

2 2

3 3 3

4 4 4 4

n .... n

((21))

Put the pie in the oven and start both clocks. When the first one runs out, turn it over. (Elapsed time: 4 minutes.) Turn the second one over when it, too, runs out. When the first one runs out again (8 minutes) the second clock has been running for 1 minute since you restarted it, so turn it over once again. When the 1 minute runs out the pie is ready.

((22))

McGinity outsmarted himself. True enough, McGillicuddy definitely will not start and the choice lies between him and McGivern. But, as he has no way of knowing *why* McGillicuddy won't start, the information cannot affect his chances. They remain the same—1 in 3—while *McGivern's* go up to 2 in 3.

Examine the chances why the manager said "McGillicuddy won't start."

A) Because McGivern will start: $\frac{1}{3}$

B) Because McGinity will start: $\frac{1}{3} \times \frac{1}{2}$ (coin came up tails) = $\frac{1}{6}$

Calculation confirms that his chances of starting are one half those of McGivern's.

((23))

The next express stop on the IRT 7th Avenue Subway is 96th Street.

((24))

The difference in elevation equals the sum $66\frac{2}{3} + \frac{66\frac{2}{3}}{7} + \frac{66\frac{2}{3}}{7 \times 7}$ and so on without end. This is a geometric series of first term $A = 66\frac{2}{3}$ and ratio $R = \frac{1}{7}$. Though there be an infinite number of terms in a geometric series, the limit of the sum is always finite and equal to $\frac{A}{1 - R}$ if, and only if, R^2 is less than 1.

In this case the sum equals

$$\frac{66\frac{2}{3}}{1 - \frac{1}{7}} = 7 \times 11.111 \ldots$$

which is 77.777 . . ., or exactly $77\frac{7}{9}$ feet.

If this is your first experience with infinite geometric series you might like to solve the puzzle of the hunter who became lost in the woods and wandered about in "circles."

He left his camp and walked 1 mile east, then ½ mile north, ¼ mile west, ⅛ mile south, then again east for ¹⁄₁₆ mile, and so on in this manner until he wound up (literally) at—well, where did he wind up?

The answer is listed as Numerical Answer Number 62.

((25))

Paradoxical puzzles of this type go back to the Golden Age of Greece. According to Samuel Putnam, Cervantes' superbly erudite American translator, they again enjoyed great vogue during Spain's Golden Age. Here is how the subtlety was disposed of by Cervantes:

> "Well, then," said Sancho, "my opinion is this: that part of the man that swore to the truth should be permitted to pass and that part of him that lied should be hanged, and thus the letter of the law will be carried out."
>
> "But, my Lord Governor," replied the one who had put the question, "it would be necessary to divide the man into two halves, the lying half and the truthful half, and if he were so divided it would kill him and the law would in no wise be fulfilled. . . ."
>
> "See here, my good sir," said Sancho, "either I am a blockhead or this man you speak of deserves to die as much as he deserves to live and cross the bridge; for if the truth saves him, the lie equally condemns him. And this being the case, as indeed it is, it is my opinion that . . . since there is as much reason for acquitting as for condemning him, they ought to let him go free, as it is always more praiseworthy to do good than to do harm. . . . When justice was in doubt [Don Quixote advised me] I was to lean to the side of mercy; and I thank God that I happened to recollect it now, for it fits this case as if made for it."
>
> —*Don Quixote,* Part II, Chapter LI

((26))

The first puzzle *is* perhaps "too easy." Select one bean from the box labeled "RB." That is the one and only pick you must make. Both beans in that box are of the same color, now determined by the pick. Remove the "RB" label and *switch* it with the correct one taken from one of the other two boxes. Now switch the labels on those two boxes. All three boxes are now correctly labeled.

Note that the beans could not have been distributed one red and one black bean in each box, for then the "RB" label would have been truthful.

The second puzzle presents another of those marvelous "paradoxes" of probability where seemingly irrefutable logic is indeed specious. It is actually twice as likely that the second bean in the box will also be red rather than black. Start with the draw itself. I might just as likely have picked a black bean. Regardless of the color picked then, it is twice as likely that I drew the bean from a "solid" box ("RR" or "BB") as that I drew from the "mixed" box ("RB"). Another way of looking at it is to reason that if I picked a red bean it is twice as likely to have come from the "RR" box than from the "RB" box, there being two reds in the former and only one in the latter.

If you still do not accept this answer (2 chances in 3 the second bean is also red) get out three coffee mugs and six checkers and try it yourself a couple of dozen times.

Incidentally, though the reasoning presented in the puzzle exposition is certainly the most common solution offered, it is not the only erroneous one I have heard. An outstanding engineer once astounded me with the answer that it is 1½ times as likely the second bean would be *black,* there being five undetermined beans after the draw, 3 black and 2 red!

((27))

Of the first two statements one is true and the other false. Statement D cannot be true without contradicting itself. Whether C is true or not, the final statement cannot be false without contradicting either C or D. Conclusion: you are a very logical person. A flattering deduction, but is it true?

Suppose statement E were changed to an obvious falsehood such as "Black is white." We would then encounter paradox, just as Sancho Panza did (Puzzle Number 25) and just as the Greek logicians did when Epimenides of Crete first shouted "All Cretans are liars!"

A good deal of work has been done by modern thinkers such as Russell and Whitehead in an effort to circumvent these paradoxes and to bring logic within a formalized mathematical system. From Gödel we get the "Uncertainty Principle," which tells us that a system which deals with itself encounters paradox, that its postulates cannot be verified within the system.

The answer to the puzzle, then, is that the truth of statement E is uncertain. "True ideas," wrote William James, "are those we can assimilate, validate, corroborate and verify."

((28))

There are six continuous routes which pass through all eight zones once. Starting in a given zone each route may be traversed two ways, making a total of twelve different ways to take *le tour du monde*.

The solution is greatly simplified by using a schematic representation of the divided globe:

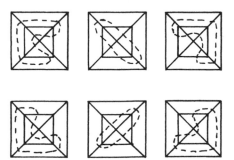

SUPERIOR MATHEMATICAL PUZZLES

The inner square represents the equator; the outer one represents the South Pole. The diagonals divide the squares into the eight zones, while their intersection forms the North Pole. The broken lines are the routes to be taken.

((29))

The easiest way I know of solving this problem makes use of the fact that the ratio of the distances traveled by the courier and the army in the same time is the ratio of their speeds.

The diagram below shows the relative positions of the courier and the army at the start, when the message is delivered, and when the courier returns to the rear.

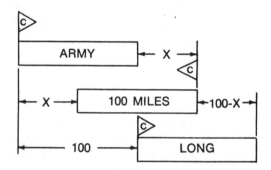

When the courier reaches the front the army has gone X miles, the courier $100 + X$ miles. In the time the army goes $100 - X$ miles, completing its 100-mile march, the courier rides the X miles to the rear. Thus, the courier rides $100 + 2X$ miles in all.

Since the ratio of their speeds is constant,

$$X : 100 + X :: 100 - X : X$$

which reduces to

$$X^2 = 5000$$
$$X = \sqrt{5000}$$
$$X = 70.71$$

Therefore, the total distance traveled by the courier is

$$100 + 2(70.71) \text{ miles, or } 241.42 \text{ miles.}$$

((30))

Using	1	flag(s)	there	are		3	distinct	signals
"	2	"	"	$3 \times 2 =$	6	"	"
"	3	"	"	$6 \times 2 =$	12	"	"
"	4	"	"	$12 \times 2 =$	24	"	"
"	5	"	"	$24 \times 2 =$	48	"	"
"	6	"	"	$48 \times 2 =$	96	"	"

For a total of 189 distinct signals.

However, of the 48 signals of 5 flags, $3 \times 2 \times 1 \times 2 \times 1 = 12$ require 3 flags of one color, and of the 96 signals of 6 flags there are 66 which cannot be made with only 2 flags of each color. Deducting these there remain 111 distinct signals possible.

((31))

A)
```
   49
   68
   T2
   LL
  100
  396
```
The duodecimal sum is 3 9 6

He should bake three gross, nine doz., & six loaves altogether.

B) The dimensions of the table in duodecimal notation are simply 2.53 feet by 3.14 feet. The area is

```
      2.53
  (×) 3.14
      9 90
      2 53
      7 3 9
   7.7 0 00  sq. ft. (=
```
decimal $7\,7/12$ sq. ft.)

C) The only correct completion is

```
       7L
   (×) 34
      278
      1L9
     2248
  (−) 4T2
     1966
```

If you found these three little puzzles too vexatious, don't put the blame on a "primitive" system. (Because twelve has more factors than ten it is possibly superior.) Lay it, rather, to the fact that you were never taught "new" math.

((32))

If you take one "hemisphere" and make a straight cut from the base to the apex, you will be able to lay the lateral surface of the cone flat. (Have you ever made a coolie hat?) The plane figure formed is a circle with a pie-shaped sector removed. (See below.) Its radius is the length of the cut (the slant height of the cone), L = 5,000. The central angle of the sector removed is $\frac{L - R}{L} \times 360$

(where R is the base radius of the cone), or $\frac{360}{5}$

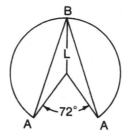

In the figure, A and B are two points on the equator 180 degrees apart, and it is not difficult to compute the straight-line distance between them at 9,511 miles.

This is the shortest distance between Topsy and Turvy. If you went over either pole the distance would be 10,000 miles; around the equator, over 12,500 miles. And, when you take the straight-line course you have a choice of four routes, two in each "hemisphere."

((33))

The radius of film on the slower reel is 1½ times as large as the radius of the film already projected. The running times are proportional to the areas of film; the areas to the squares of the radii. Time remaining = $\frac{3}{2} \times \frac{3}{2} \times \frac{16}{3}$ = 12 minutes.

Too straightforward? Consider, then, the rolling wheel shown below.

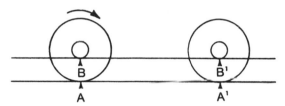

A is a point on the rim of the wheel and *B* a point on the hub. When the wheel has made one complete revolution *A* is at A^1. The horizontal distance traveled is evidently equal to the circumference of the wheel. But, the hub has also made one complete revolution — the distance traveled equals the circumference of the *hub*. Conclusion: the hub is as large as the wheel!

This paradox was treated by Galileo in his *Discorsi* . . . *(Dialogues Concerning Two New Sciences)* back in the seventeenth century. Can you explain it?

((34))

Divide the balls into three groups of four. For the first weighing match one group against a second. If they do not balance, the four balls on the down side are potentially heavy (mark each one with an *H)*, the four balls on the up side are potentially light (mark each one with an *L)*, and the four balls in the third group are definitely normal (mark each one with an *N)*. If they do balance then the four balls in the third group are potentially odd (mark each one with an *O)*, and the eight balls on the scale are all normal. The procedure for ferreting out the oddball in each case follows.

101

CASE I—Imbalance in First Weighing

1. Weigh *LHN* against *LLH*.   Place *LHH* aside. There are three possible outcomes: (A) they balance; (B) the left side goes down; (C) the left side goes up.

2. If (A), then the oddball was placed aside. Which of the three it is can be determined by weighing the two *H*'s against each other. If (B), then either the *H* on the left side or one of the two *L*'s on the right side is the culprit. Weigh the two *L*'s against each other to find out. If (C), then either the *L* on the left side or the *H* on the right side is the oddball. Weigh one of them against an *N* to find out.

CASE II—First Weighing Balances

1. Weigh *OO* against *ON*.   Place *O* aside. There are three possible outcomes: (A) they balance; (B) the left side goes down; or (C) the left side goes up.

2. If (A), then the *O* placed aside really is odd. Weigh it against an *N* to determine whether it is heavy or light. If (B), weigh the two *O*'s on the left side against each other. If they do not balance, the heavy ball is obvious. If they do balance, then the *O* on the right side in step 1 is light. If (C), the two *O*'s on the left side are potentially light and the *O* on the right side is potentially heavy. Follow the same procedure as for (B).

((35))

This is one of the nicest rate problems devised by the great American "puzzleer" Sam Loyd (1841-1911). He gives an algebraic solution, but it is more fun to deduce the answer.

Setting out at the same time from the way station the coach could spot you 1 mile. Setting out first from the station you get a 30-minute head start and beat the coach by 15 minutes: it could afford to spot you only 15 minutes. Your speed is, therefore, 1 mile in 15 minutes.

The distance from Tucson to the station is 4 miles plus the distance you can walk in 30 minutes while the coach waits, or 6 miles in all.

Since the coach could spot you 30 minutes to the station but only 15 minutes from there to Deadwood, the distance from the station to Deadwood is half of 6 miles, or 3 miles.

From Tucson to Deadwood it is 6 plus 3, or 9 miles in all. The coach's speed is 6 mph; walking speed is 4 mph.

((36))

The tricks depend on the fact that the sum of the digits zero through nine is divisible by nine, and the sum of the digits in a number divisible by nine is also divisible by nine.

In the first trick the sum of the digits in the year is the same as the sum of the digits in the transposed number. Their difference is always divisible by nine. The sum in the second trick must also be divisible by nine. No matter what you multiply them by, the end result will be a multiple of nine. Charley used your weight and age for multipliers to try and con you; he could have used the number of fleas on his dog Rube.

To find the missing digit, then, Charley adds up the digits in your answer and subtracts the sum from the next higher multiple of nine. In the first trick 24 from 27 is 3; in the second trick 8 and 1 are 9. This process, which all good bookkeepers know, is called, "casting out nines."

(Obviously, if you erase a 0 or a 9, Charley would have to guess between them. Thus only "nine out of ten times.")

((37))

1	tentacle(s) at a time there are	$\dfrac{8^2}{1}$	=	64	ways to kiss
2	"	$\dfrac{(8 \times 7)^2}{2 \times 1}$	=	1,568	"
3	"	$\dfrac{(8 \times 7 \times 6)^2}{3 \times 2 \times 1}$	=	18,816	"
4	"	$\dfrac{(8 \times 7 \times 6 \times 5)^2}{4 \times 3 \times 2 \times 1}$	=	117,600	"

and so on, in this manner.

If you took the trouble to complete the calculation then you know there are 1,441,728 ways in which two octopi can kiss. At two seconds per kiss, it would take them over a month to complete the routine!

For a truly astounding result in the realm of permutations, however, consider the problem of determining the number of different ways in which a $5 bill can be changed. (A $1 bill can be changed in 293 distinctly different ways using pennies, nickels, dimes, quarters, halves, and silver dollars.) You will find the octopus to be a piker compared to the miser who set this puzzle and is still to be found in his countinghouse buried beneath an avalanche of money.

((38))

Start with a 3-4-5 triangle and subtract 3 square units as shown:

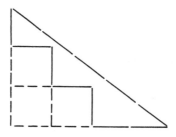

While you still have those twelve matches handy, arrange them to make the following pattern:

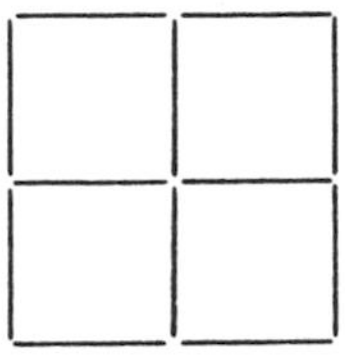

Now, by changing the position of three of the matches, can you remove one square? All twelve matches must be used and the altered pattern is simply three instead of four unit-area squares.

Time limit: 60 seconds.

((39))

With two of the six chambers loaded, the first player's chances of dying are ⅓ and his chances of living ⅔. If the first player survives, the second has 2 chances in 5 of drawing a bullet. The only way the second player can die is for both events (first survives, second draws a bullet) to occur. His chances of dying are therefore ⅔ × ⅖ = 4/15 and his chances of living 11/15.

There is only a slight advantage (11/15 to 10/15) in going second.

The probability that both players survive is not 11/15 × 10/15, as the 11/15 includes chances where the first player dies, but ⅔ × ⅗ = ⅖ (first player survives, second draws a blank).

It is interesting to note that if only one bullet were used and, again, unlike Russian roulette, two adjacent chambers were fired without revolving the cylinder between shots, there would be no advantage in going second.

((40))

On any field a certain number of cows will be required just to keep the growth down. Let fewer than this number graze and the field will be overrun; a greater number, and it will be grazed bare. Thus:

X cows graze the steady growth of 10 acres;

24−X cows graze the existing grass on 10 acres bare in 2 weeks;

12−X cows graze the existing grass on 10 acres bare in 6 weeks;

from which,

$$2(24 - X) = 6(12 - X)$$
$$X = 6 \text{ cows}$$

We see that 12 cows will just keep down the growth of 20 acres. The answer to the farmer's question is, therefore, "Forever"—so long as England remains a "green and pleasant land."

((41))

Scott is the copilot, Carpenter the navigator, Gordon the pilot, and Cooper the engineer.

((42))

The boys make 6 cents profit on every 5 papers sold, or 6/5 cents per paper. Let X be the number of papers Johnny sold, and Y be the total number sold by all three boys. Johnny's total earnings are

$$\frac{6}{5} \cdot \left(\frac{X}{2} + \frac{Y}{6} \right)$$

Willy and Sammy together earned

$$\frac{6}{5} \cdot \left(\frac{Y-X}{2} + \frac{Y}{3} \right)$$

106

Since the difference in their earnings was $1,

$$\left(\frac{Y-X}{2} + \frac{Y}{3}\right) - \left(\frac{X}{2} + \frac{Y}{6}\right) = \frac{5}{6} \cdot 100$$

$$2Y - 3X = 250 \qquad (I)$$

For Johnny to make up the dollar he would have to sell Z *extra* papers on Tuesday. He would keep $\frac{2}{3}$ the profit on them, and $\frac{1}{3}$ would go to Willy and Sammy:

$$\frac{1}{3} \cdot \frac{6Z}{5} = 100$$

$$Z = 250$$

$$X + 250 = Y + 25 \qquad (II)$$

Simultaneous solution of equations I and II yields $X = 200$, $Y = 425$.

Johnny sold 200 papers, Willy sold 100, and Sammy sold 125.

((43))

Let D denote the distance equivalent of the 8-second head start. In the time Flip backstrokes $50 - 2 - D$ yards, Dolph backstrokes 50 yards and free-styles 2, which is the same as $50 + (\frac{2}{3})2$ yards all backstroke. Then Dolph will free style the remaining 48 yards in the time Flip backstrokes 2 yards and free-styles $50 - 14$, which is the same as $36 + (\frac{3}{2})2$ yards all free style.

Since the ratio of their backstroke speeds is the same as the ratio of their free-style speeds,

$$\frac{48 - D}{50 + \frac{4}{3}} = \frac{39}{48}$$

$$D = {}^{151}/_{24} \text{ yards}$$

The total head start Dolph can afford to give is D plus the distance Flip can backstroke in the time he, Flip, can free-style 14 yards, or

$$^{151}/_{24} + (\frac{2}{3})14$$

which is exactly $15\frac{5}{8}$ yards.

((44))

Averaging the times for a result of 1 minute is incorrect in either case.

In 1½ minutes the man can walk down 1 moving escalator or up 3. In 3 minutes' walking, half the time up and half the time down, he can walk 4 escalator lengths. This is his walking pace — 4 escalator lengths in 3 minutes — for the effect of the moving escalator is canceled. He can therefore climb (or descend) the still escalator in ¼ of 3 minutes, or 45 seconds.

In the 1½ minutes required to walk down the moving "up" escalator he walks the equivalent of 2 still escalators. Therefore the escalator must have moved up once in that time and its speed is 1 length in 1½ minutes.

((45))

Let X = the number of hits, and Y = the number of at-bats. Then

$$\frac{Y}{X + Y} = \frac{3}{2} \cdot \frac{X}{Y - X}$$

Since we are seeking a ratio we need only select an arbitrary value of one unknown, say X = 1, and solve the equation for the corresponding value of the other unknown, Y. If you fail to see this, you can still solve the equation directly for the ratio X/Y, the batting average:

$$\frac{X}{Y} + 1 = \frac{2}{3} \left(\frac{Y}{X} - 1 \right) \qquad \text{Let } r = \frac{X}{Y}$$

$$r + 1 = \frac{2}{3} \left(\frac{1}{r} - 1 \right)$$

$$3r^2 + 5r - 2 = 0$$

$$(3r - 1)(r + 2) = 0$$

$$r = \frac{1}{3}$$

The shortstop is batting a respectable .333.

108

((46))

If M denotes the number of missile shares, P the number of power shares, and U the number of uranium shares to be purchased, the following equations can be written:

$$30M + 20P + .50U = 1000 \qquad (I)$$
$$M + P + U = 100 \qquad (II)$$

The only positive integer solution (see Puzzle Number 10) is $M = 17$, $P = 23$, and as befits a speculator, the greatest number $U = 60$.

((47))

Oscar has, in effect, weighed two marlins. On one end of the rope the marlin he caught, and an imaginary one of the same weight on the other end to balance it. The restraint of the dock which keeps the hoisted marlin up is the "imaginary" one, but the force it exerts on the scale is real.

Oscar should have tied the free end of the rope to the marlin also. Then he would have gotten a true weight of 62½ pounds (unaffected by the weight of the rope and pulley).

The story is, of course, fictitious. Pacific marlin run over 1,000 pounds.

((48))

Let X be the number of pecks Peter picks in one hour. From the first statement, Peter and Paul pick 3 pecks together in one hour; Paul picks $3 - X$. From the second statement, Paul and Priam pick 2 pecks together in one hour; Priam picks $2 - (3 - X) = X - 1$. From the third statement, Priam and Peter pick 1½ pecks together in one hour; Peter picks $1½ - (X - 1) = 2½ - X$.

$$X = 2½ - X$$
$$X = 1¼.$$

Peter picks 1¼ pecks in one hour, or 1 peck in 48 minutes.

109

((49))

The figure below is a cross section of the pyramid taken perpendicular to the ground through a diagonal of the base layer.

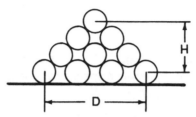

The distance D is the diagonal of a 3-foot square (consider a view looking down on the base layer), which is $\sqrt{18}$, or $3\sqrt{2}$. H is half of D, and the total height, H + 1, equals 3.12 feet.

Here's a "quicky" to try before going on to the next one: By changing the position of three of the ten balls in the pyramid above, can you turn it upside down? This is what it should look like:

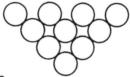

Time limit: 60 seconds.

((50))

Two triangular pyramids—one of four layers and one of three—containing 20 and 10 balls, respectively, may be made from the 4-by-4 square-based pyramid with no balls left over.

The general rule is this: any regular tetrahedron of n layers may combine with another of $n - 1$ layers to form a square-based pyramid of n layers. The number of balls in a regular tetrahedron of n layers is $\dfrac{n(n + 1)(n + 2)}{6}$. The number of balls in a square-based pyramid of n layers is the sum of the squares of the numbers 1 through n. (See Puzzle Number 20.)

Employing a procedure similar to the one used in the previous puzzle, the vertical height of a triangular pyramid is found to be $1 + (n - 1)\sqrt{2/3}$ (if the diameter of the ball is 1 foot).

The height of the taller pyramid is thus $1 + (3)\sqrt{2/3} = 3.45$ feet.

((51))

M. de G., the poorest shot, will probably survive. His chances are better than even if he duels *wisely.* This means firing into the air if the draw selects him to shoot first. For to shoot first and kill either Mr. J. or Mr. K. invites certain death from the other.

Whichever of the two marksmen shoots first will kill the other one. Then M. de G.'s life will depend on whether he hits (60%) or misses (40%) the remaining marksman. M. de G.'s chances of survival are therefore 60%; the remaining 40% is split equally (before the order is drawn) between Mr. J. (20%) and Mr. K. (20%).

If M. de G. allows rancor to blur his reason and decides, if given the first shot, to shoot at either Mr. J. or Mr. K., his chances of survival become less than even. It is then more likely that one of the two marksmen survive (52%) — if *they* shoot wisely — than it is that M. de G. will (48%).

Are there any lessons to be learned here?

((52))

The number of possible arrangements of the 26 letters is $26 \times 25 \times 24 \ldots \times 1$. In each of the arrangements there are 23 positions in which the word "IAGO" can appear. For each position the 22 remaining letters can be arranged in $22 \times 21 \ldots \times 1$ ways. The probability that the name "IAGO" appears is therefore

$$\frac{23 \times 22 \times 21 \ldots \times 1}{26 \times 25 \times 24 \ldots \times 1} = \frac{1}{15,600}$$

Since the appearance of "IAGO" excludes the possibility that "LEAR" will also appear—the letter A being common—the probability that one or the other appears is the sum of their individual chances, or 1 in 7,800.

We have kept our monkey from striking any one key more than once. If we let him strike any four keys with the possibility the same key may be struck more than once the probability he will type "IAGO" or "LEAR" is

$$\frac{2}{26 \times 26 \times 26 \times 26} = \frac{1}{228,488}$$

As you approach the task Huxley set for his monkeys the odds increase, but not the difficulty of mathematical expression. It is in fact easy to determine the number of books which they can type.

If the keyboard contains 30 selected characters from which an intelligible version of any book can be composed, and if a book is defined as containing 1,000 pages of 50 lines, at 60 characters to the line, then the number of different books they can eventually produce is:

$$30^{60^{50^{1000}}} = 30^{3,000,000} \text{ books.}$$

Somewhere within that incomprehensibly large but finite collection will be found not only the works of Shakespeare, but every book ever written, every book that ever will be written, and every book that never was and never will be written!

((53))

The accompanying figure shows the area swept out by the tether—fixed at C and kept taut—as it unwinds then winds again around the silo from and to point A.

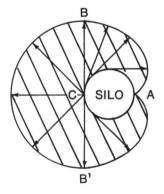

The length of the tether equals half the circumference of the silo, pi R, where R is the radius of the silo.

The area to the left of line B-B¹ is a semicircle of radius equal to the tether length. Its value is $\dfrac{R^2 \; pi^3}{2}$

The area* bounded by the involute A-B, the silo, and the line B-C is

$$\frac{R^2 \cdot pi^3}{6}$$

The total area grazed is then

$$\frac{5}{6} \cdot R^2 \cdot pi^3 = 2{,}580 \text{ square feet}$$

*Finding the area beneath an involute is a challenging recreation in calculus. To begin with, the parametric equations of the curve are

$$X = R \cos \Theta + R \Theta \sin \Theta$$
$$Y = R \sin \Theta - R \Theta \cos \Theta$$

with the origin at the center of the silo, O, and R its radius. If the taut tether is tangent to the silo at a point "P," then the parameter Θ is the angle made by O-P with the X axis.

((54))

Let $\;Q$ = the amount of moonshine in the cask at any time T.

$\dfrac{dQ}{dT}$ = the rate of change of Q with respect to T.

-1 = the rate at which the mixture of moonshine and water leaves the cask, gallons per minute.

Then,

$$\frac{dQ}{dT} = \frac{-Q}{100}$$

Solution of this differential equation yields

$$Q = 100 \times e^{-T/100}$$

where e is the base of natural logarithms.

When T = 10 minutes, Q = 90.48 gallons. The amount of moonshine stolen is $100 - Q = 9.52$ gallons; the amount of water, .48 gallons.

((55))

If you are unfamiliar with the methods of calculus used below in determining the general equation of the "pursuit curve" — the path of the torpedo — skip right to the end, for the answer is surprising and simple.

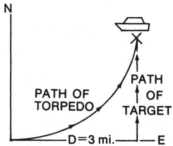

Using rectangular coordinates with the torpedo fired from the origin, the target vessel starts at (D,0) and moves along the line $X = D$. Let K be the ratio of the speed of the target to the speed of the torpedo. At any instant the torpedo is at (X,Y) a distance S from the origin measured along the curve, and the target has moved a distance KS. The tangent to the curve at (X,Y) passes through the position of the target (D,KS) and the following equations can be written:

$$\frac{dY}{dX} = \frac{KS - Y}{D - X} \tag{I}$$

$$\frac{dS}{dX} = \sqrt{1 + \left(\frac{dY}{dX}\right)^2} \tag{II}$$

Differentiating equation I with respect to X results in

$$(D - X)\frac{d^2Y}{dX^2} = K\frac{dS}{dX} \tag{III}$$

Substitute II into III to get

$$(D - X)\frac{d^2Y}{dX^2} = K\sqrt{1 + \left(\frac{dY}{dX}\right)^2} \tag{IV}$$

Equation IV may be solved by successive integrations to yield the general equation of the pursuit curve:

$$2Y = \frac{D^{-K}(D-X)^{K+1}}{K + 1} - \frac{D^K(D-X)^{1-K}}{1 - K} + \frac{KD}{K + 1} + \frac{KD}{1 - K} \tag{V}$$

114

When the torpedo catches up to the target at $(D,\overline{Y})$ only the last two terms of the right-hand side of equation V remain:

$$2\overline{Y} = \frac{KD}{K+1} + \frac{KD}{1-K} \qquad\text{(VI)}$$

where $\overline{Y}$ is the distance traveled by the target vessel.

The distance traveled by the torpedo, $\overline{S}$, is thus given by

$$2\overline{S} = \frac{D}{K+1} + \frac{D}{1-K} \qquad\text{(VII)}$$

The significance of this last equation is stunningly simple: Twice the distance traveled by the torpedo equals the distance it would have to travel if the target were moving west (directly toward it) plus the distance it would have to travel if the target were moving east (directly away from it)!

With the target 3 miles away and moving half as fast as the torpedo, the distance traveled in pursuit is half of ⅔ of 3 miles plus half of twice 3 miles, or 4 miles in all.

((56))

Consider the room to be a cardboard carton which may be folded flat. This can be done in several ways—three are shown below—and a straight line route drawn between the spider and the fly.

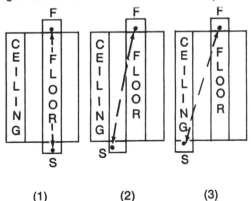

| (1) | (2) | (3) |

Route 1 provides the most popular answer to this problem, 42 feet, but it is not the correct one. There are two routes still shorter. Route 2, 40.7 feet, and route 3, the shortest, which provides the correct answer of 40 feet.

It may seem odd, but the shortest route will take the spider across 5 of the 6 surfaces of the room!

((57))

In this solution, it is not at all necessary to consider the speeds of the boats. When the boats meet the first time, together they have traveled the width of the river once. When they meet a second time, they have together traveled three widths and each boat has gone three times as far as it did when they first met.

The boat which set out at the start from the near shore has covered the width of the river plus 400 yards. This must be three times the 720 yards it had covered when they first met. The width of the river is therefore 400 yards shy of 2,160 yards, which is exactly one mile.

((58))

Here again, as in Puzzle Number 3, it is simpler to find first the chances two people will *not* share the same birthday.

Each person may be born on any of 365 days, one date just as likely as another (birth statistics aside, and no leap years, either, in puzzleland).

A list of the 30 birthdays would contain one of 365^{30} different possible arrangements. The number of arrangements possible in which each person has a different birthday is $365 \times 364 \ldots \times 336$. The probability, then, that no two people share the same birthday is

$$\frac{365 \times 364 \ldots \times 336}{365^{30}}$$

which is .30 (very nearly).

The probability that someone does share a birthday is $1 - .30 = .70$.

It is $2\frac{1}{3}$ times as likely that someone will share a birthday as it is that all 30 people will have different birthdays!

Try and check the theoretical odds empirically next time you are at a gathering. You could include as few as 24 people, and the odds would still favor (but barely) a shared birthday.

A secondary puzzle is suggested: How many people must there be in the room before it becomes probable that among them someone is celebrating his birthday that very same day? (The answer is listed as Numerical Answer Number 63.)

((59))

One reason why this puzzle was a favorite of Carroll's was no doubt the diversity of incorrect answers, stubbornly insisted upon, that it educed.*

Loyd claimed that as the monkey climbed it would fall with increasing speed. Others, that the weight would fall, or would have no effect whatsoever. The actual result is that no matter how the monkey climbs, the weight will always be opposite him (assuming for simplicity only that the weight and monkey are directly opposite at the start). The force the monkey exerts on the rope to lift himself will raise the weight an equal distance. Even if the monkey were to let go, fall, and catch the rope again, he would still find himself opposite the weight, for both weight and monkey would fall with the same acceleration.

*For an appreciation of Lewis Carroll the mathematician, see the May 1956 issue of *Scientific American*. This particular puzzle is mentioned, among many others, in that issue.

((60))

This is another favorite puzzle by Lewis Carroll. It appears in *The Lewis Carroll Picture Book,* edited by Stuart Dodgson Collingwood.

1. Lower weight.
2. Lower son, raise weight.
3. Lower weight.
4. Lower pig and cat, raise weight.
5. Lower daughter, raise son and pig.
6. Lower weight.
7. Lower son, raise weight.
8. Lower dog, raise cat.
9. Lower weight.
10. Lower pig and cat, raise weight.
11. Lower queen, raise son, pig, and cat.
12. Lower weight.
13. Lower pig and cat, raise weight.
14. Lower weight.
15. Lower son, raise weight. All have now been successfully lowered to the ground.

Since this puzzle appears in the Carroll book without solution, I would appreciate hearing from anyone who can bring the entire family and menagerie down in fewer moves than shown above.

((61))

There are people who occasionally leave off work on their perpetual-motion machines long enough to come up from the basement and try to square a circle or trisect an angle. They are wasting their time: both these geometric problems have long since been proved to be impossible of solution. It can't be done—without trickery.

The catch here is in the words "all the time in the world." The classic problem of trisecting an angle requires you to do it in a finite number of constructions. The method which follows requires in theory an infinite number of steps, though in practice only a few for a sufficiently accurate solution.

Starting with any angle, if you take away ½ of it, add back ¼, take away ⅛, add ¹/₁₆, and so on endlessly, you will wind up with ⅔ of the angle. In other words, ⅔ is the sum of the infinite geometric series of 1st term 1 and ratio $-$ ½.

The diagram below illustrates this method of trisecting any angle by successive bisections.

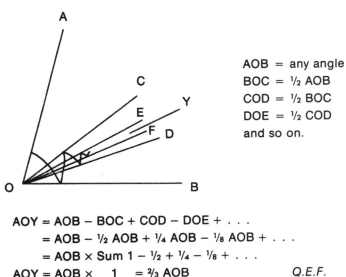

AOB = any angle
BOC = ½ AOB
COD = ½ BOC
DOE = ½ COD
and so on.

AOY = AOB $-$ BOC + COD $-$ DOE + . . .

$\quad$ = AOB $-$ ½ AOB + ¼ AOB $-$ ⅛ AOB + . . .

$\quad$ = AOB × Sum 1 $-$ ½ + ¼ $-$ ⅛ + . . .

AOY = AOB × $\dfrac{1}{1 + \frac{1}{2}}$ = ⅔ AOB $\qquad$ Q.E.F.

NUMERICAL ANSWERS

(1)   Four colors

(2) $2

(3)   175/256

(4)   36 and 72 mph.

(7)   377 pairs

(8)   40 sq. yds.

(10) 78 and 62 coins

(12) 40 minutes

(13) 4,000 gals.

(16) 7/24

(18) 46 and 20

(19) 20

(20) 2,030,100 sq. in.; 25,502,500 cu. in.

(22) 0, $\frac{1}{3}$, $\frac{2}{3}$

(23) 96

(24) 77 $\frac{7}{9}$ ft.

(26) $\frac{2}{3}$

(27) Maybe

(28) 12 ways

(29) 241.42 miles

(30) 111

(32) 9,511 miles

(33) 12 minutes

(35)   9 miles

(36)   3, 1

(37)   1,441,728

(39)   2nd; 40%

(42)   200, 100, and 125

(43)   15 ⅝ yds.

(44)   45 sec.; 90 sec.

(45)   .333

(46)   17, 23, and 60

(47)   62½ lbs.

(48)   48 minutes

(49)   3.12 ft.

(50)   3.45 ft.

(52)   1 in 7,800

(53)   2,580 sq. ft.

(54)   9.52 and .48 gals.

(55)   4 miles

(56)   40 ft.

(57)   1 mile

(58)   7:3 in favor

(The next two answers belong to the additional problems that were raised in Solutions 24 and 58 respectively.)

(62)   .4 mi. N.; .8 mi. E.

(63)   253